To Francoise Malby Anthony
& the entire Thula Thula Wild Team

Printed in the United States of America

First Printing, 2016

ISBN 978-1-943880-06-5
Library of Congress Control Number 2016935201

Bluefox Press
Saratoga Springs, UT 84045

Bluefoxpress.com

My Baby Rhinos

The Story of Kelsey's African Adventure!

By Kelsey Paul & Jill Paul

Illustrations by Chelsea Jones
& her 6th grade art class

 an imprint of
BlueFox Press

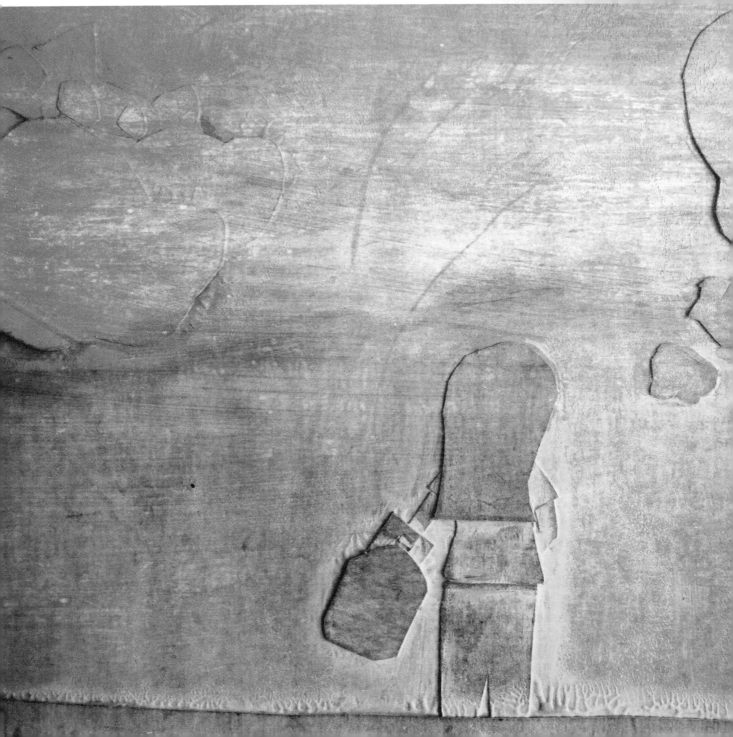

"Africa!" they said,
I was excited to hear

Even though the long flight
filled me with fear.

But "Yes!" I said, knowing
adventure would come

Hanging with the elephants
was bound to be fun.

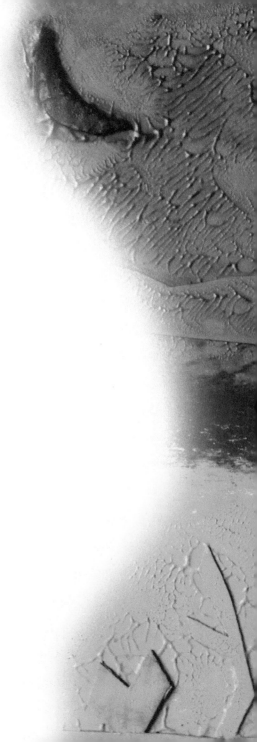

On our first night,
dining under the stars,

It was time to walk back,
our room not too far.

Our guide said, "Oh no,
by yourselves, don't you dare,"

With flashlight in hand,
he led with great care.

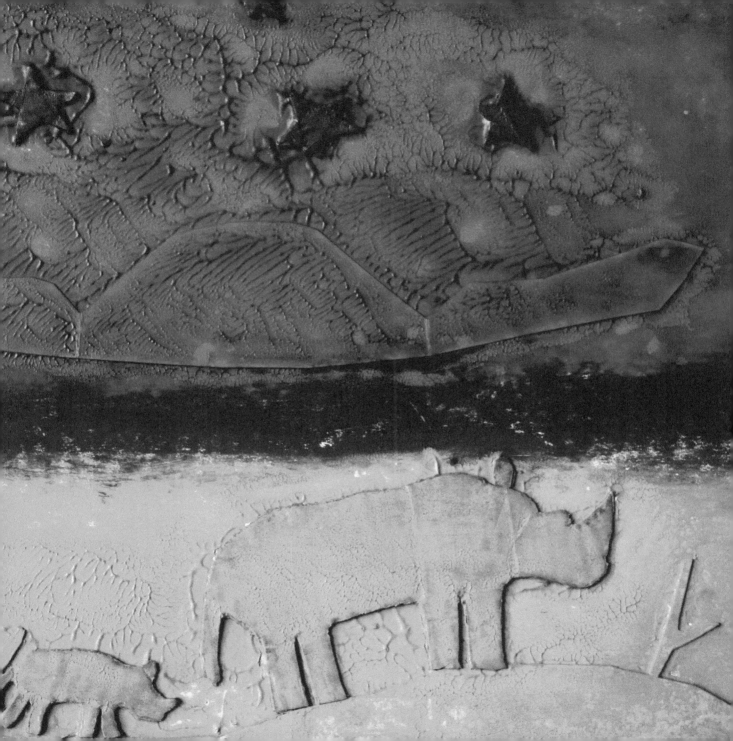

"Look over there,
do you see the grey mounds?"

We crept forward in silence,
not making a sound.

"The orphaned rhinos," he said,
"they come back each night."

Asleep under our window,
what a great sight!

All curled up together,
looking so sweet,

So excited our first night-
wow, what a treat!

Morning came early,
at the first sign of light,

"Are they still there?"
I asked with delight.

They heard us waken,
they knew it was time,

We were excited,
but they were just fine.

Grazing on grass,
no worries about us.

Can we get to breakfast
without making a fuss?

"They're Thabo and Ntombi,"
said Victor our ranger.

"White Rhinos, our goal
is to keep them from danger."

"See the two guards?
They stay day and night,

To protect them from hunters,
never leaving their sight."

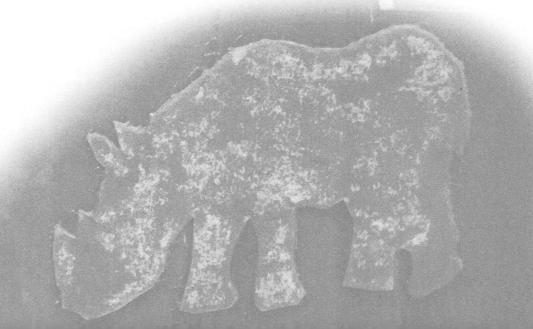

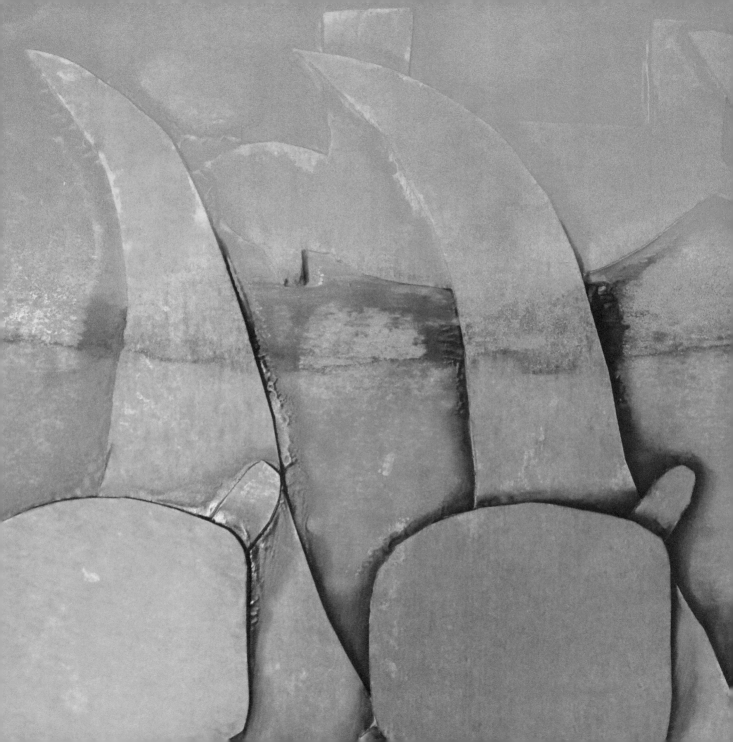

"But why would they need
to be guarded all the time?

With those big sharp horns,
they should manage just fine!"

"Aw", Victor explained,
"It's the horns that they steal.

Some think they're like medicine,
but the cure isn't real."

"Please tell us their story,
how they came to be,

How they each got here,
their whole history."

"Thabo came to us,
in the stormy dark cold,

losing his mother
when just one day old."

"He stole all our hearts
with his terrible cry,

He was there without his mom
and didn't know why."

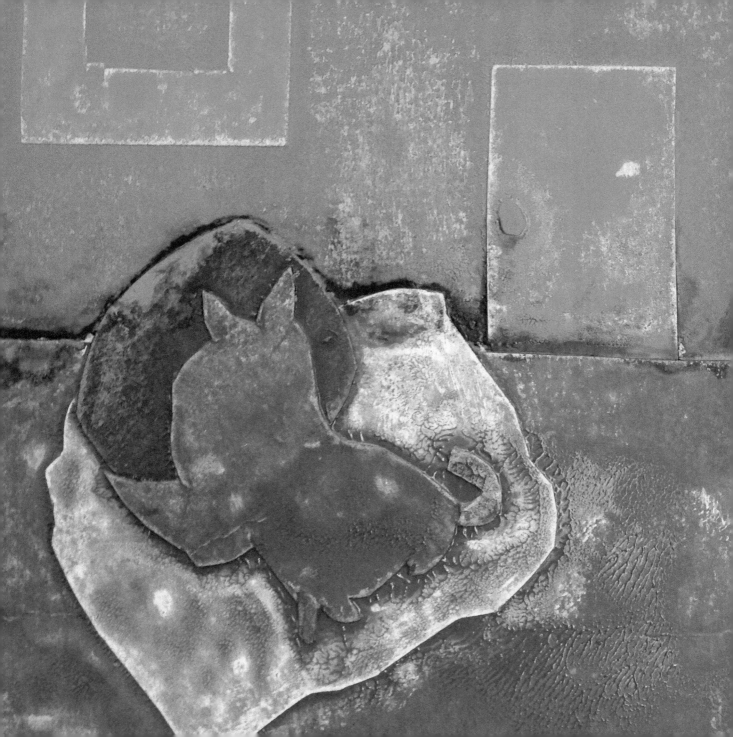

"We'll give him some blankets,
he can sleep near the bed."

But wanting more comfort,
he jumped up instead.

And he jumped and he jumped
breaking bed after bed,

Just wanting to cuddle,
a pillow for his head.

He played with his keepers,
full of mischief and fun,

But as his horn grew,
they knew they were done!

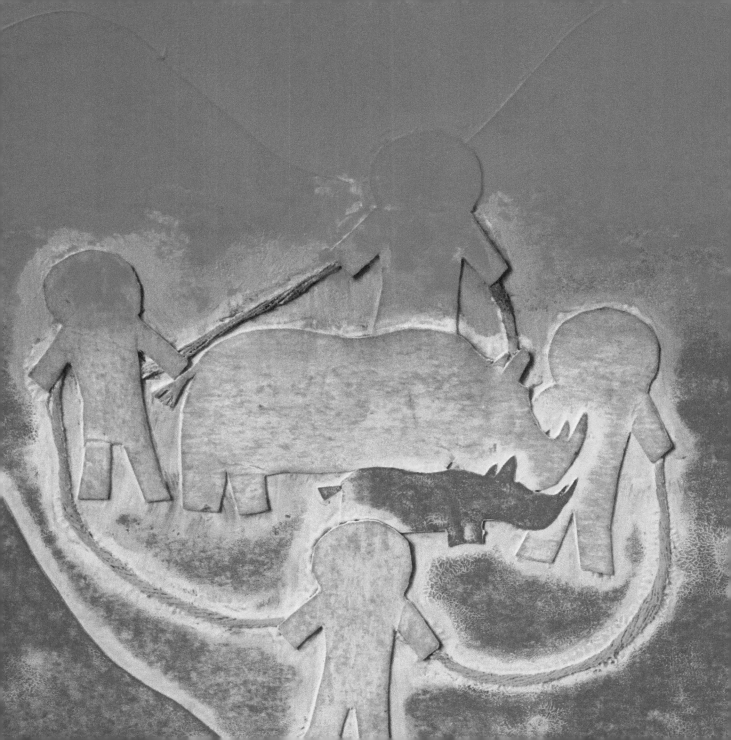

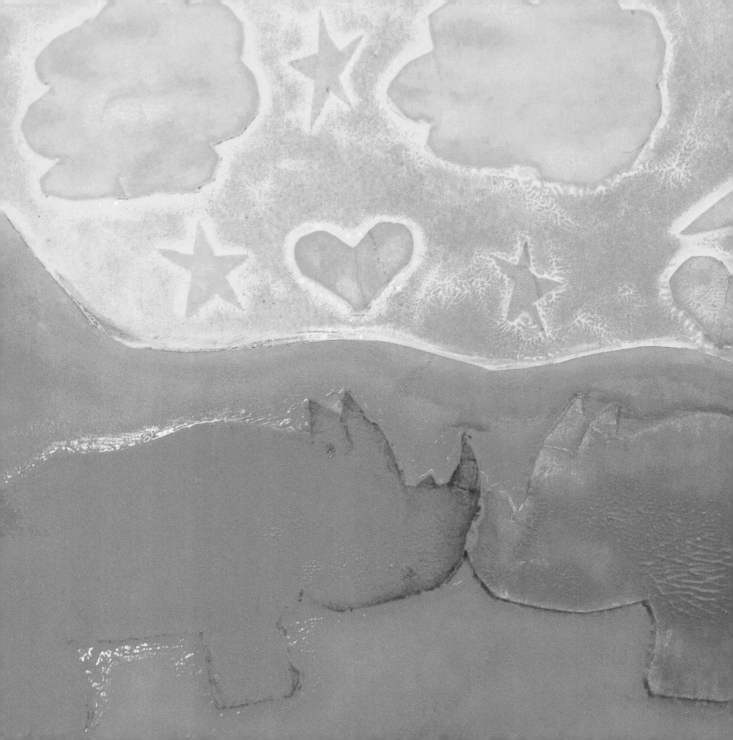

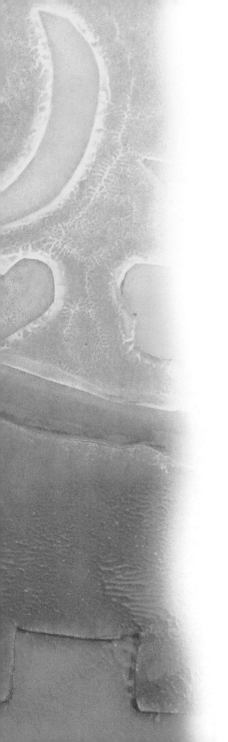

A companion for Thabo,
sweet Ntombi her name,

Thabo was curious,
did he look the same?

A boy and a girl,
how perfect are they?

Maybe they'll have
some babies one day?

"We loved them and raised them
until they were steady,

And released them to the wild
when we thought they were ready."

"The hunters found Thabo,
while out in the wild

He was shot in the leg,
while still just a child."

"We found him in time
and he was okay,

But protection they now needed
for both night and day."

A decision was made:
"We must save the others,

Let's build an orphanage
for those without mothers."

"A place for the babies,
whose parents were taken

We'll build it right here,"
their commitment unshaken.

So up on the hill,
Victor drove us to see

A new wildlife orphanage,
what a home it would be!

Their love for these animals,
so strong and so deep,

An awareness I knew
I needed to keep.

So on my flight home,
the memories so clear,

I vowed to return
without any fear.

I now had a mission,
but what could I do?

Raise money to help?
I hadn't a clue.

Those boxes of T-shirts,
given to us by a friend,

Print a rhino design–
a message we'll send!

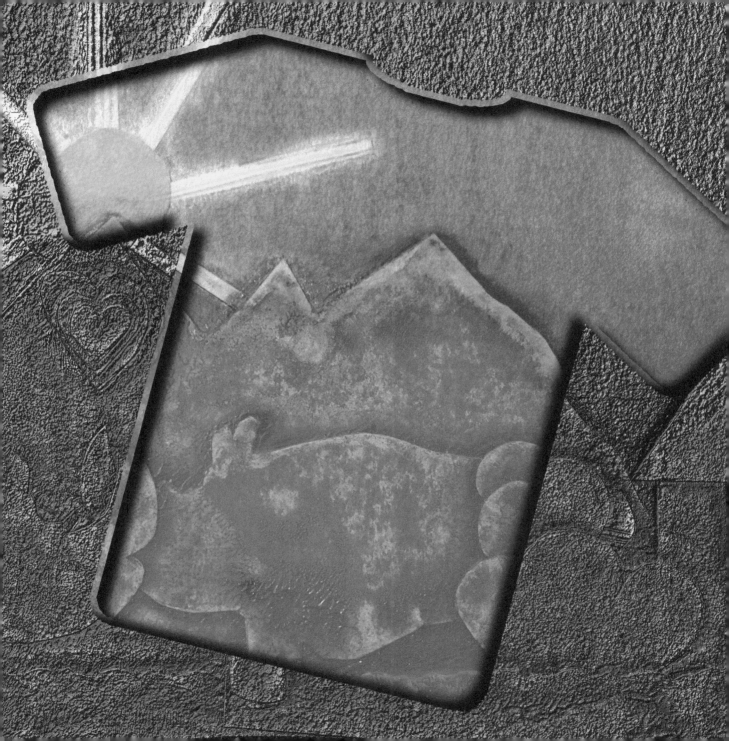

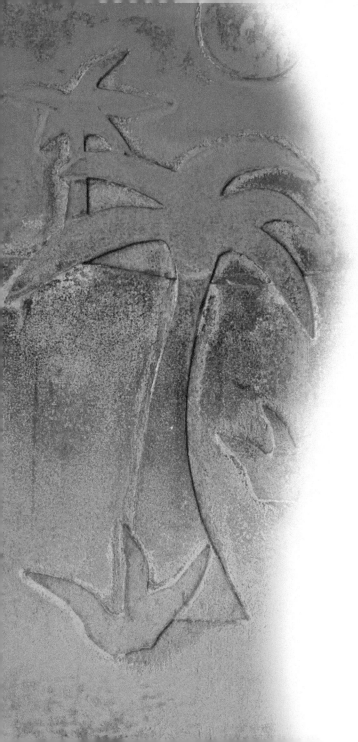

So sell them we did
at the high school bazaar.

The community said, "Yes!"
what heroes they are.

If people at home could feel the great need,
How far could I throw the next little seed?

A book for all children, read by their own mothers,
We'll tell them our story, they'll tell it to others.

In English, in Zulu, in German, in Dutch,
In Chinese, Vietnamese, they'll love it so much.

So that is my dream, to make the whole world aware,
That rhinos like humans deserve love and care.

In memory of Lawrence Anthony

...and his love for Nana who started this journey for all of us

"It is about the elephants - it was they who
whispered to me and taught me how to listen."

-The Elephant Whisperer by Lawrence Anthony

How you can make a difference too!

-Share Kelsey's story with your family and friends to raise awareness

-Share the Facebook Pages: My Baby Rhinos - The Story of Kelsey's African Adventure and
Thula Thula Wildlife Rehabilitation Centre

-Create a project like Kelsey did to raise funds and spread awareness

-Donate at www.thulathula.com/conservation-fund/
Any amount counts!

-Send your friends a gift of
"My Baby Rhinos - Kelsey's African Adventure!"
100% of author proceeds go to the Thula Thula Wildlife Rehabilitation Centre

Congratulations! You have made a difference!!

Special thanks to our artists!

Jack Abuhaidar
Brigitte Davis
Phoebe Anderson
Alysandra Garcia
Hazel Catley
Carmen Gasparik
Akacia Christoffersen
Myah Dale
Ava Kelly
Macey Olden
Liina Koch
Ainsley Shaw
Kathleen Whiteley
Madeline Lytle
Olivia Toronto
Briley Wade
Sarah Page
Ms. Chelsea Jones

CPSIA information can be obtained
at www.ICGtesting.com
Printed in the USA
LVHW071400190121
676877LV00016B/564

9 781943 880065